Sea tongue

Kevin Crossley-Holland

Illustrated by Clare Challice

BBC/LONGMAN

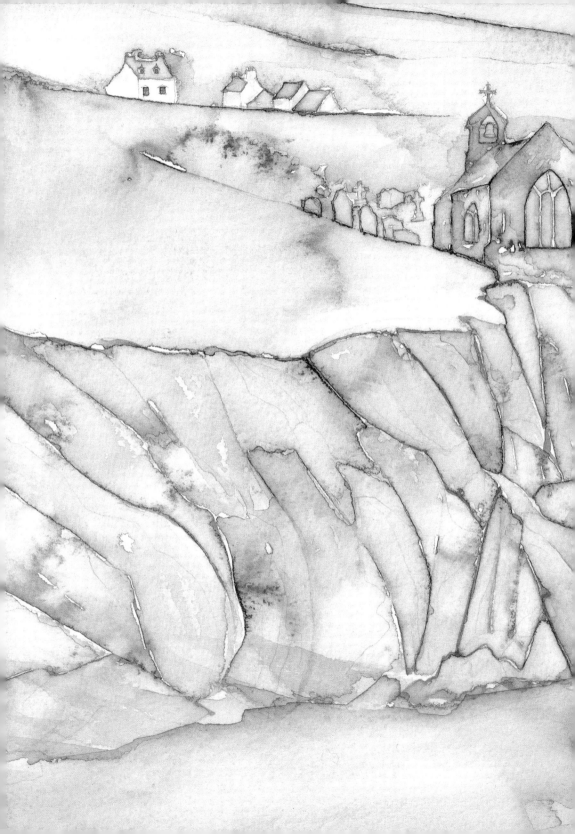

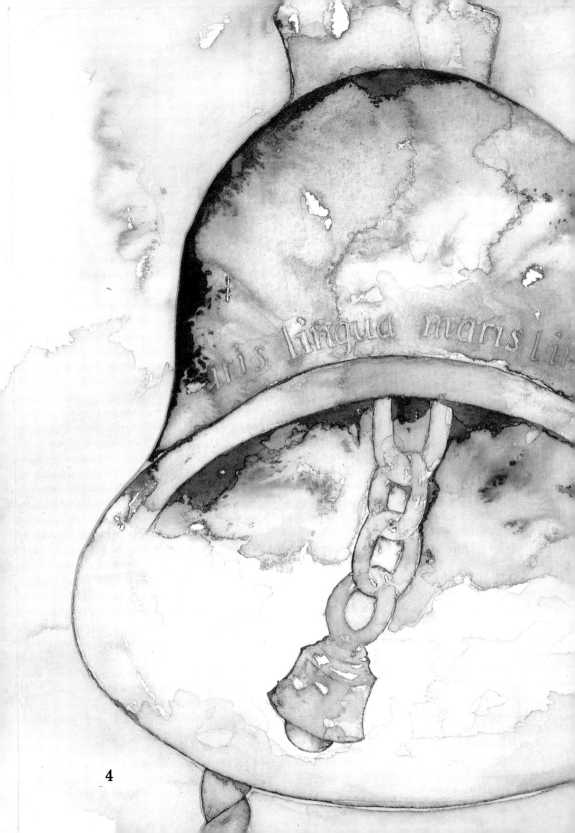

4

I am the bell. I'm the tongue of the bell. I was cast before your grandmother was a girl. Before your grandmother's grandmother. So long ago.

Listen now! I'm like to last. I'm gold and green, cast in bronze, I weigh two tons. Up here, in the belfry of this closed church, I'm surrounded by sounds. Mouthfuls of air. Words ring me.

High on this crumbling cliff, I can see the fields of spring and summer corn; they're green and gold, as I am. I can see the shining water, silver and black, and the far fisherman on it. And look! Here comes the bellringer – the old bellwoman.

6

I am the bellwoman. For as long as I live I'll ring this old bell for those who will listen.

Not the church people: they have all gone. Not the seabirds; not the lugworms; not the inside-out crabs nor the shining mackerel. Whenever storms shatter the glass or fogs take me by the throat, I ring for the sailor and the fisherman. I warn them off the quicksands and away from the crumbling cliff. I ring and save them from the sea-god.

7

I am the sea-god. My body is dark; it's so bright you can scarcely look at me, so deep you cannot fathom me.

My clothing is salt-fret raised by the four winds, twisting shreds of mist, shining gloom. And fog, fog, proofed and damp and cold. I'll wrap them round the fisherman. I'll wreck his boat.

I remember the days when I ruled earth. I ruled her all – every grain and granule – and I'll rule her again. I'll gnaw at this crumbling cliff tonight. I'll undermine the church and its graveyard. I'll chew on the bones of the dead.

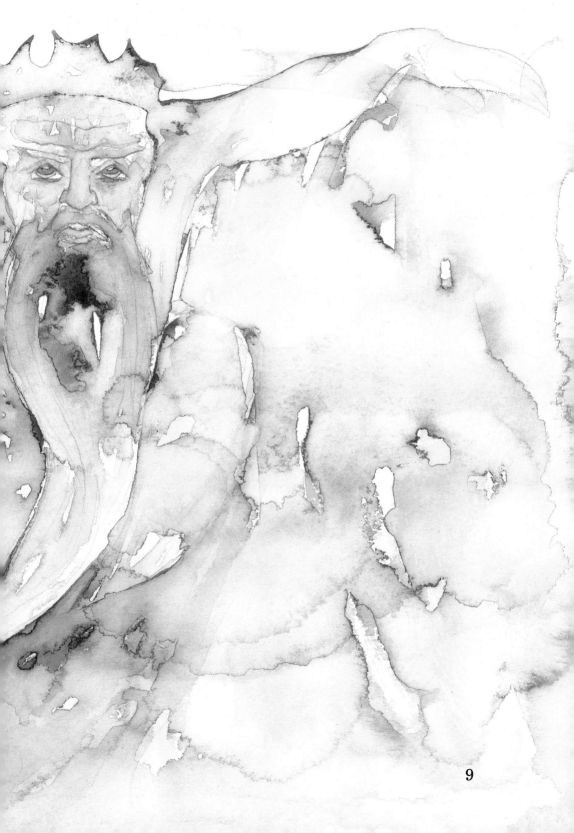

9

10

We are the dead. We died in bed, we died on the sword, we fell out of the sky, we swallowed the ocean.

To come to this: this green graveyard with its rows of narrow beds. Each of us separate and all of us one.

We lived in time and we're still wrapped in sound and movement – gull-glide, gull-swoop. We live time out, long bundles of bone bedded in the cliff.

I am the cliff. Keep away from me.
I'm jumpy and shrinking, unsure
of myself. I may let you down badly.

Layers and bands, boulders and
gravel and grit and little shining
stones: these are earth's bones.
But the sea-god keeps laughing
and crying and digging and
tugging. I scarcely know where I
am and I know time is ending.

Fences. Red flags. Keep away from
me. I'm not fit for the living.

We are the living. One night half of a cottage –
Peter's cottage – bucketed down into the boiling
water and he was left standing on the cliff-edge in
his night-shirt.

After that, everyone wanted to move inland.
We had no choice. You've only to look at the cracks.
To listen to the sea-god's hollow voice!

Every year he comes closer. Gordon's cottage went
down. And Martha's. And Ellen's. The back of the
village became the front. And now what's left?
Only the bellwoman's cottage, and the empty shell
of the church.

I am the church.

I remember the days when the bellows
wheezed for the organ to play. I remember
when people got down on their knees
and prayed.

I've weathered such storms. Winds
tearing at the walls, flint-and-brick, salt
winds howling.

And now, tonight, this storm. So fierce,
old earth herself is shaking and shuddering.
Ah! Here comes the old bellwoman.

17

I am the bellwoman. There! Those lights,
stuttering and bouncing. There's a boat out there,
and maybe ten.

Up, up these saucer steps as fast as I can. Up!

Here in this mouldy room, I'll ring and ring and
ring, and set heaven itself singing, until my palms
are raw. I'll drown the sea-god.

19

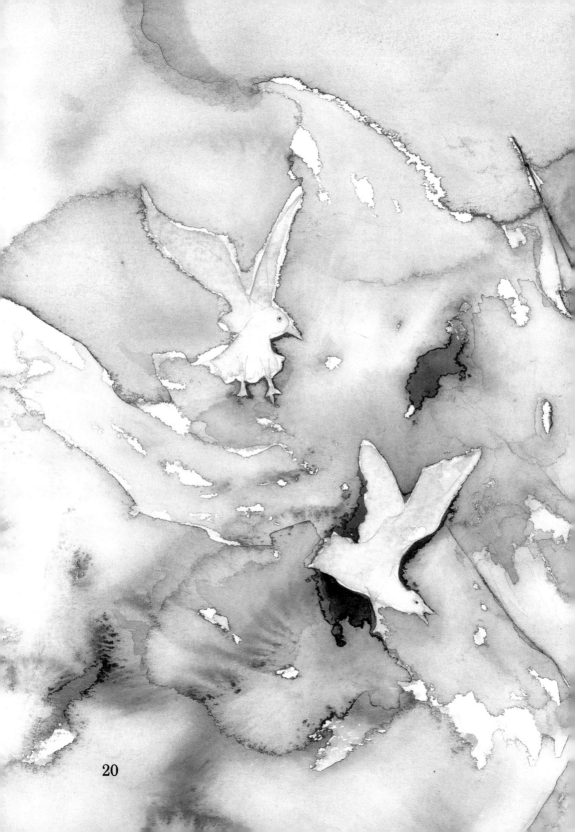

20

I am the sea-god. And I keep clapping my luminous hands.

Come this way, fisherman, over the seal's bath and here along the cockle-path. Here are the slick quicksands, and they will have you.

Fisherman, come this way over the gulls' road and the herring-haunt! Here, up against this crumbling cliff. Give me your boat.

I am the boat.
To keep afloat; to go
where my master tells me:
I've always obeyed the two
commandments.

Now my master says forward but
the sea-god says back; my master says
anchor but the night-storm says drag. My deck is
a tangle of lines and nets and ropes; my old heart's
heavy with sluicing dark water. I'm drowning; I'm torn apart.

Groan and creak: I quiver; I weep salt. Shouts of the
fishermen. Laughter of the sea-god. Scream of the night-storm.

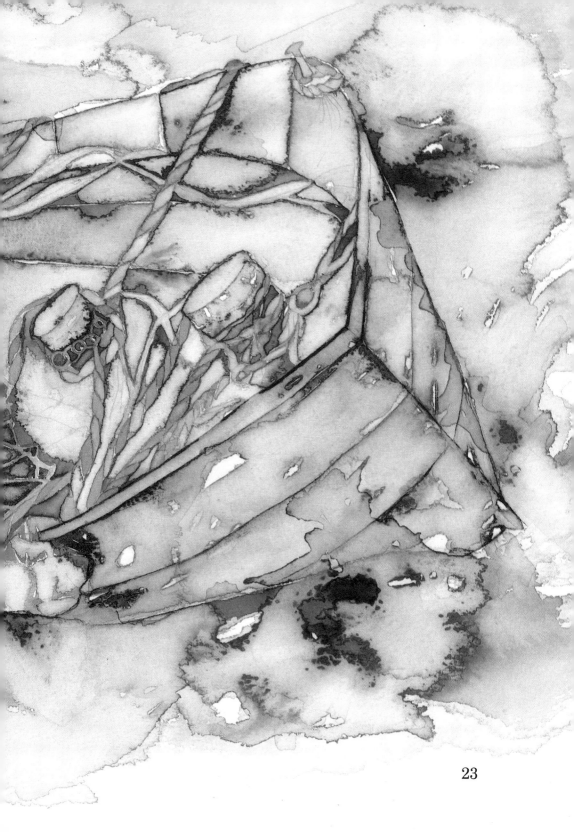

23

24

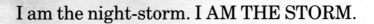

I am the night-storm. I AM THE STORM.

Down with the bell and down with the belfry.
Down on the white head of the bellwoman. Down
with the whole church and the tilting graveyard.
Down with the cliff itself, cracking and opening
and sliding and collapsing. Down with them all
into the foam-and-snarl of the sea.

I'm the night-storm
and there will be no morning.

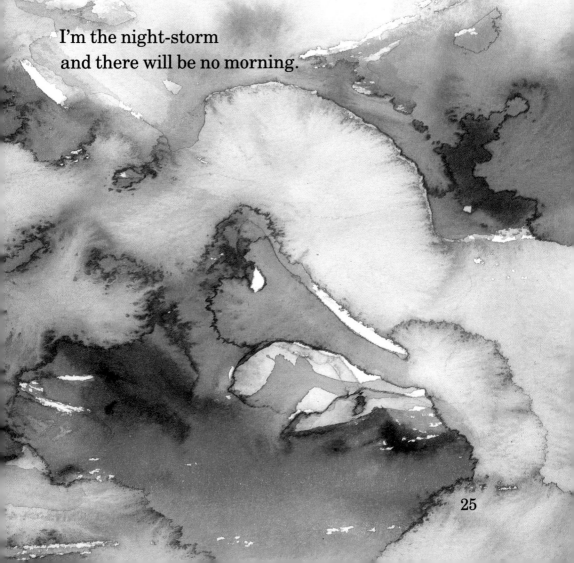

26

I am the morning. I am good morning.

My hands are white as white doves, and healing.
Let me lay them on this purple fever. Let them
settle on the boat. Nothing lasts for ever. Let me
give you back your eyes, fisherman.

I am the fisherman. I heard the bell last night.
Joe and Grimus and Pug, yes we all did! I heard
the bell and dropped anchor. But there is no bell.
There's no church, there's no belfry along this
coast. Where am I? Am I dreaming?

Well! God blessed this old boat and our haul of
shiners. He saw fit to spare us sinners. We'll take
our bearings now, and head for home.

But I heard the bell. And now! I can hear it! Down,
down under the boat's keel. I can hear the bell.

28

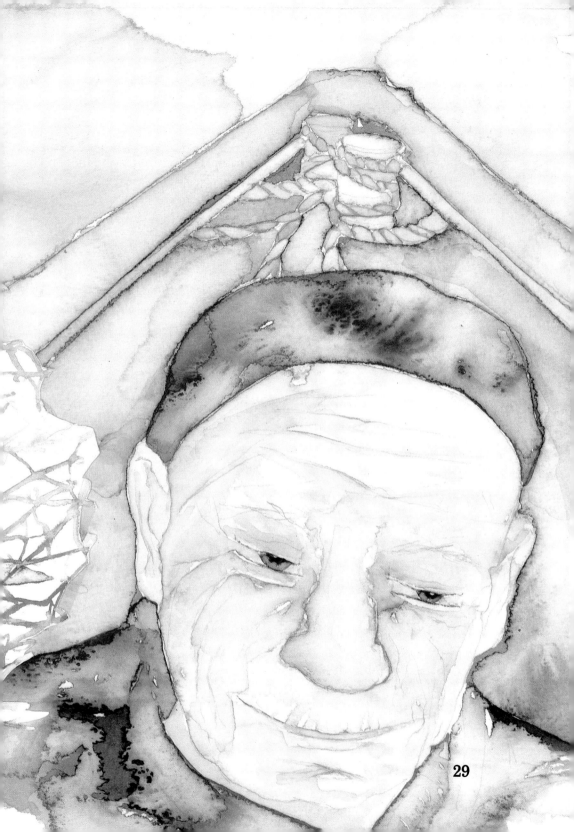

29

I am the bell. I am the tongue of the bell, gold and green, far under the swinging water.

I ring and ring, in fog and storm, to save boats from the quicksands and the rocky shore. I'm like to last; I'm cast in bronze, I weigh two tons.

Listen now! Can you hear me? Can you hear the changes of the sea?

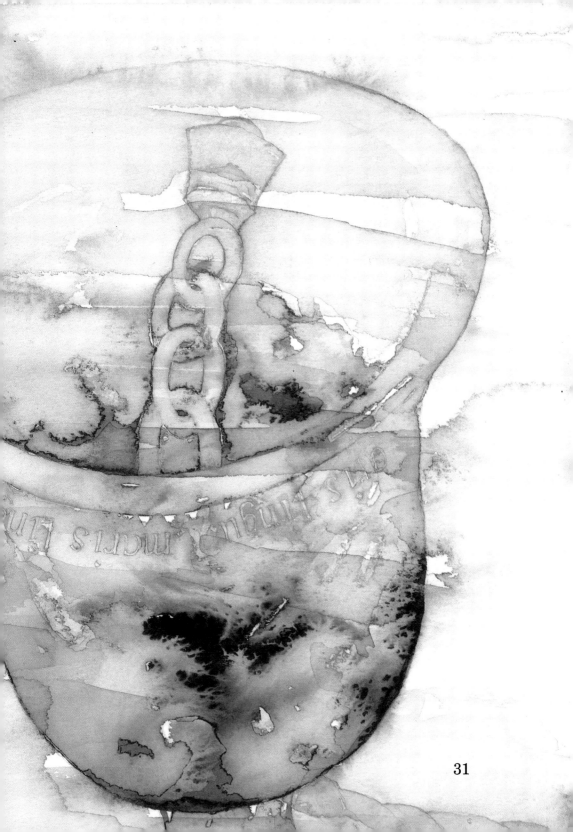

Other titles in this series

Isn't my name magical? Poems by James Berry
Trellie the troog by Douglas Hill
The porcelain man by Richard Kennedy
Caruso's cool cats by Dick King-Smith
Cap o' Rushes by Alison Lurie
Dare's secret pony by Emma Tennant
Owl by Diana Wolkstein

Series consultants: Myra Barrs and Sue Ellis, Director and Deputy Director of the Centre for Learning in Primary Education (Southwark).

The series accompanies the BBC School Radio series, *Listening and Reading* on Radio 5 Medium Wave.

Published by BBC Educational Publishing and Longman Group UK Limited

BBC Educational Publishing
a division of
BBC Enterprises Limited
Woodlands
80 Wood Lane
London W12 0TT

Longman Group UK Limited
Longman House
Burnt Mill
Harlow
Essex CM20 2JE
England and associated
companies throughout the world

First published in 1991
© BBC Enterprises Limited/Longman Group UK Limited 1991
Text © Kevin Crossley-Holland 1991
Illustrations © Clare Challice 1991

Series editor Joan Griffiths
Cover and book design by
Jo Digby
(school edition) ISBN 0 582 06233 0
(trade edition) ISBN 0 563 34785 6

Set in 14/18 Century Schoolbook
Typeset by Goodfellow and Egan
Text and cover origination by
Dot Gradations
Printed and bound by Cambus Litho